Bilingual Language, Speech, and Special Education Dictionary

Larry J. Mattes

**Academic
Communication
Associates**

P. O. Box 4279
Oceanside, CA 92052-4279

**Academic
Communication
Associates, Inc.**

P. O. Box 4279
Oceanside, CA 92052-4279

WEB: http://www.acawebsite.com
E-Mail: acom@acadcom.com
Telephone Order Line: (888) 758-9558
Fax: (760) 722-1625

Printed in the United States of America
Product Number: 4037
International Standard Book Number: 978-1-57503-146-0

Table of Contents

Introduction

The *Bilingual Language, Speech, and Special Education Dictionary* was created to meet the needs of speech-language pathologists, audiologists, learning disability specialists, school psychologists, and other special education professionals who work with students from Spanish language backgrounds. Many Spanish-speaking students in our schools come from homes where Spanish is used most or all of the time. If the student's parents have limited knowledge of English, assessment and program placement information must be provided in their native language.

Meeting the needs of Spanish-speaking students is often a challenge in school programs because of the limited availability of professionals who speak Spanish fluently. Those who speak Spanish may not have sufficient knowledge of the terminology necessary to translate forms or write instructional objectives (Mattes & García-Easterly, 2007; Roseberry-McKibbin, 2008). This dictionary was created to fill a need for a concise, easy-to-use resource that professionals can use to locate and learn special education terms in both English and Spanish. This dictionary includes a variety of terms commonly used when communicating with parents and writing instructional objectives for students identified as having communication disorders or language-based learning difficulties. Researchers interested in developing assessment and instructional materials in the Spanish language should also find this dictionary to be a useful reference.

The terms in this dictionary were selected based on a review of program placement forms, test manuals, textbooks, and classroom curriculum standards. Terms from the *Bilingual Language, Speech, and Hearing Dictionary* (Mattes, 2000) are among those included in this resource. A variety of new terms have been added relevant to communication disorders, reading disabilities, and the academic goals of the classroom curriculum.

This dictionary includes both an *English-Spanish* section (Part 1) and a *Spanish-English* section (Part 2). The English and Spanish terms have been placed in separate columns on each page so that this resource can be used as a study aid. Students learning Spanish terminology, for example, can do the following:

1. Cover up the Spanish column with a piece of paper.
2. Read each English word and write the Spanish equivalent on the piece of paper.
3. After translating all of the terms on the page, remove the piece of paper so that the recorded answers can be checked for accuracy.

The *Bilingual Language, Speech, and Special Education Dictionary* includes terms that will be helpful to professionals in planning intervention programs, translating forms, and designing instructional resources. It is important to remember, however, that a variety of Spanish dialects are spoken in the United States. Therefore, the content of this dictionary should be reviewed by speakers of the various dialects used within the local community so that appropriate modifications can be made.

Professionals from the fields of bilingual education, speech-language pathology, medicine, and special education provided input that was helpful in selecting items for this practical resource. The author is especially grateful to Cristina Saldaña-Illingworth, Alfredo Ratniewski, Rosa Ratniewski, George Santiago, and Sonia Verdes for their valuable contributions and comments.

Part 1

English - Spanish

A

abduction	abducción
ability	habilidad
ability test	examen de aptitud
abnormal	anormal
abnormality	anormalidad
academic	académico
accent	acento
achievement	aprovechamiento, rendimiento, logro
achievement age	edad de logro
achievement test	prueba de nivel
acoustic reflex	reflejo acústico
acoustics	acústica
Acquired Immune Deficiency Syndrome	síndrome de inmunodeficiencia adquirida
active short term memory	memoria a plazo corto activa
activities of daily living	actividades de la vida cotidiana

acuity	agudeza
acute head trauma	traumatismo de craeal agudo
adaptive behavior	conducta adaptativa
adduction	aducción
adjective	adjetivo
adverb	adverbio
affricate	africada
age norm	norma de edad
age scale	escala de edad
age score	puntaje (puntuación) de edad
age-equivalent	equivalente de edad
aggressive behavior	conducta agresiva
aglossia	aglosia
agnosia	agnosia
agrammatism	agramatismo
agraphia	agrafia
air conduction	conducción aérea
air conduction threshold	umbral de conducción aérea
airway	vía respiratoria

alalia	alalia
allomorph	alomorfo
allophone	alófono
alphabet	alfabeto
alternative assessments	pruebas alternativas de evaluación
alveolar	alveolar
Alzheimer's Disease	enfermedad de Alzheimer
American Sign Language	lenguaje de señas estadounidense
amnesic aphasia	afasia amnésica
amplification	amplificación
analogy	analogía
analysis of variance	análisis de varianza
anarthria	anartria
aneurism	aneurisma
annual goal	meta anual
annual review	revisión anual
anomia	anomia
antisocial behavior	conducta antisocial
antonym	antónimo

anxiety	ansiedad
anxiety attack	ataque de ansiedad
anxiety disorder	trastorno de ansiedad
aphasia	afasia
aphasic	afásico
aphonia	afonía
aphonic	afónico
apraxia	apraxia
apraxic	apráxico
aptitude	aptitud
arithmetic disorder	trastorno aritmético
articulation	articulación
articulation disorder	trastorno de articulación
articulation error	error de articulación
articulation test	prueba de articulación
artificial larynx	laringe artificial
artificial palate	paladar artificial
aspirate	aspirar
assessment	evaluación

assessment plan	plan de evaluación
assimilation	asimilación
asthma	asma
Attention Deficit Disorder	trastorno de atención deficiente
attention span	capacidad de concentración
audible	audible
audiogram	audiograma
audiological evaluation	evaluación audiologica
audiologist	audiólogo
audiology	audiología
audiometer	audiómetro
audiometry	audiometría
audition	audición
auditory acuity	agudeza auditiva
auditory association	asociación auditiva
auditory behavior	conducta auditiva
auditory blending	mezcla auditiva
auditory comprehension	comprensión auditiva
auditory discrimination	discriminación auditiva

auditory disorder	trastorno auditivo
auditory feedback	retroalimentación auditiva
auditory memory	memoria auditiva
auditory ossicles	osículos auditivos
auditory perception	percepción auditiva
auditory perceptual disorder	trastorno perceptivo auditivo
auditory processing	procesamiento auditivo
auditory reception	recepción auditiva
auditory sequence	secuencia auditiva
auditory sequencing	encadenamiento auditivo
auditory skills	destrezas auditivas
auditory stimulation	estimulación auditiva
auditory training	entrenamiento auditivo
augmentative and alternative communication	comunicación aumentativa y alternativa
augmentative communication	comunicación aumentativa
augmentative communication system	sistema de comunicación aumentativa
autism	autismo
autism spectrum	espectro autista
autistic	autístico

autistic child (child with autism)

niño autista (niño con autismo)

autistic-like behavior

conducta propia del autismo

automatic expressions

expresiones automátias

automatic speech

habla automática

B

babbling

balbuceo

balanced bilingual

bilingüe balanceado

basic skills

destrezas básicas

behavior

comportamiento

behavior chart

cuadro de conducta

behavior disorder

trastorno de conducta

behavior therapy

terapia de conducta

behavioral approach

acercamiento conductual

behavioral objective

objetivo de comportamiento

bilabial

bilabial

bilingual	bilingüe
bilingual assessment	evaluación bilingüe
bilingual community	comunidad bilingüe
bilingual education	educación bilingüe
bilingual program	programa bilingüe
bilingual specialist	especialista bilingüe
bilingualism	bilingüismo
birth defect	defecto de nacimiento
birthdate	fecha de nacimiento
blends	mezclas
bone conduction	conducción ósea
bone conduction audiogram	audiograma de conducción ósea
bone conduction threshold	umbral de conducción ósea
brain damage	lesión cerebral
brain disorder	trastorno cerebral
brain tumor	tumor cerebral
breathe	respirar
breathing	respiración, respiro
Broca's Aphasia	afasia de Broca

C

cerebellum	cerebelo
cerebral dominance	dominancia cerebral
cerebral hemisphere	hemisferio cerebral
cerebral palsy	parálisis cerebral
cerebrovascular accident	accidente cerebrovascular
Certificate of Clinical Competence	Certificado de Competencia Clínica
checklist	lista de comprobación
chewing behavior	conducta de masticación
child abuse	abuso de niños
child development	desarrollo de niños
childhood trauma	trauma de niñez
chronic	crónico
chronological age	edad cronológica
circumlocution	circunlocución
classification	clasificación
classify	clasificar

clause	cláusula
cleft	hendidura
cleft lip	labio hendido
cleft palate	paladar hendido
cleft palate team	equipo de paladar hendido
clinic	clínica
clinical assessment	evaluación clínica
clinical procedures	procedimientos clínicos
clinical profile	cuadro clínico
clinician	clínico
cluster	grupo consonántico
cochlea	caracol, coclea
cochlear implant	implante coclear
code	código
code switching	cambio de código
cognition	cognición
cognitive	cognoscitivo
cognitive ability	habilidad cognoscitiva
cognitive approach	acercamiento cognitivo

cognitive style	estilo cognoscitiva
commands	mandatos, órdenes
communication	comunicación
communication difficulties	dificultades comunicativas
communication skills	destrezas de comunicación
communication style	estilo de comunicación
communicative competence	competencia comunicativa
communicative disorder	desorden comunicativo
comparative	comparativo
compensation	compensación
competence	competencia
comprehension	comprensión
concept	concepto
conceptual categories	categorías conceptuales
conceptualization	conceptualización
conditional	condicional
conduction	conducción
confidence	confianza
congenital	congénito

congenital abnormality	anormalidad congénita
conjugation	conjugación
conjunction	conjunción
consonant	consonante
consonant cluster	conjunto de consonantes
consonant deletion	omisión de consonantes
consonant reduction	omisión de grupos consonánticos
consonant sequence reduction	reducción de la secuencia de consonantes
construction	construcción
content validity	validez del contenido
context	contexto
conversation	conversación
conversation sample	muestra de conversación
copula	cópula
criterion	criterio
criterion-referenced test	prueba con referencia a criterios
criterion-related validity	validez relacionada con criterios
cultural awareness	conocimiento cultural
cultural bias	prejuicio cultural

cultural deprivation   privación cultural

cultural language   lenguaje cultural

culturally disadvantaged   culturalmente desventajado

culture   cultura

curriculum   plan de estudios, currículum

D

data   datos

deaf   sordo

deafness   sordera

decibel   decibel

decode   descifrar, decodificar

deep structure   estructura profunda

defect   defecto

deficit   deficiencia

definite article   artículo definido

definition	definición
deformity	deformidad
dementia	demencia
demonstrative	demostrativo
depression	depresión
deprivation	privación
development	desarrollo
development of language	desarrollo del lenguaje
developmental age	edad de desarrollo
developmental aphasia	afasia del desarrollo
developmental articulation disorder	trastorno del desarrollo de articulación
developmental assessment	evaluación del desarrollo
developmental deficit	déficit del desarrollo
developmental delay	atraso del desarrollo
developmental disability	discapacidad del desarrollo
developmental disorder	trastorno del desarrollo
developmental expressive language disorder	trastorno del desarrollo de lenguaje expresivo
developmental history	historia del desarrollo
developmental language disorder	trastorno del desarrollo de lenguaje

developmental levels	niveles del desarrollo
developmental milestone	hito del desarrollo
developmental norm	norma del desarrollo
developmental phonologic disorder	trastorno del desarrollo fonológico
developmental profile	perfil de desarrollo
developmental reading	lectura del desarrollo
developmental reading disorder	trastorno del desarrollo de lectura
developmental receptive language disorder	trastorno del desarrollo de lenguaje receptivo
developmental scales	escalas del desarrollo
developmental sequence	secuencia del desarrollo
developmental stage	etapa del desarrollo
deviate	desviar
deviation	desviación
diagnose	diagnosticar
diagnosis	diagnosis, diagnóstico
diagnostic center	centro diagnóstico
diagnostic instrument	instrumento diagnóstico
diagnostic procedure	procedimiento diagnóstico
diagnostic teaching	enseñanza diagnóstica

diagnostic test	prueba diagnóstica
dialect	dialecto
dialect differences	diferencias en dialectos
dialectical	dialéctico
dialectology	dialectología
dialogue	diálogo
digraph	dígrafo
diphthong	diptongo
diplacusis	diploacusia
diplophonia	diplofonía
direct object	objeto directo
disability	incapacidad
disabled	incapacitado
disacusis	disacusia
disadvantage	desventaja
discrimination	discriminación
disease	enfermedad
disorder	desorden
documentation of progress	documentación del progreso

dominant language	idioma dominante, lenguaje dominante
Down Syndrome	síndrome de Down
dysarthria	disartria
dysfluency	falta de fluidez
dysfunction	disfunción
dysgraphia	disgrafia
dyslexia	dislexia
dysphagia	disfagia
dysphasia	disfasia
dysphonia	disfonía
dyspraxia	dispraxia

E

ear	oído
earache	dolor de oído
eardrum	tímpano

echolalia	ecolalia
educable	educable
educable mentally retarded	retardado mental educable
education	educación
educational assessment	evaluación educacional
educational intervention	intervención educacional
educational measures	medidas educacionales
educational performance level	nivel de aprovechamiento académico
educational placement	colocación educativa
educational program	programa educacional
educational services	servicios educacionales
educator	educador
egocentric	egocéntrico
electroencephalogram	electroencefalograma
electroencephalograph	electroencefalógrafo
eligibility criteria	criterios de eligibilidad
embolism	embolia
emotional behavior	conducta emocional
emotional disturbance	disturbio emocional

emotional lability	labilidad emocional
encephalitis	encefalitis
encode	codificar
English as a second language	inglés como segundo lengua
enrichment	enriquecimiento
enunciation	enunciación
environment	ambiente
epiglottis	epiglotis
epilepsy	epilepsia
error	error
esophagus	esófago
ethnic	étnico
ethnic group	grupo étnico
etiology	etiología
eustachian tube	trompa de eustaquio
evaluation	evaluación
examiner	examinador
exceptional child	niño excepcional
expression	expresión

expressive	expresivo
expressive language	lenguaje expresivo
expressive mode	modo expresivo
expressive vocabulary	vocabulario expresivo
external ear	oído externo

F

facial paralysis	parálisis facial
false starts	salidas falsas
falsetto	falsete
fingerspelling	deletreo dactilar
fluency	fluencia
foreign accent	acento extranjero
form of language	forma del lenguaje
fricative	fricativa
functional disorder	trastorno funcional

functional level	grado actual de desarrollo
functional reading skills	destrezas funcionales de lectura
functional use of language	uso funcional del lenguaje

G

genetic	genétic
genetics	genética
gerund	gerundio
gesture	gesto
global aphasia	afasia global
glottal	glotal
glottis	glotis
goals	metas
grade	grado
grade equivalent score	puntaje del grado equivalente
grade level	nivel del grado

grade norms	normas del grado
grade placement	grado de colocación
grammar	gramática
grammatical	gramatical, gramático
grammatical development	desarrollo gramatical
grammatical structures	estructuras gramaticales
grammatically correct	gramaticalmente correcto
gross motor skills	habilidad motora de los músculos gruesos
group therapy	terapia de grupo

H

handicap	incapacidad, impedimento
handicapped	incapacitado, impedido
hard palate	paladar duro
head injury	lesión de cabeza
head trauma	trauma de cabeza

health assessment	evaluación de la salud
hearing	audición
hearing aid	audífono, aparato auditivo
hearing impairment	impedimento auditivo
hearing loss	pérdida de audición, pérdida auditiva
hearing test	prueba de audición
hemiplegia	hemiplejia
hereditary	hereditario
Hispanic	hispano
hoarseness	ronquera
home language	lengua materna
hypernasality	hipernasalidad
hyponasality	hiponasalidad

I

idea expression	expresión de ideas
idioglossia	idioglosia
idiom	modismo
imitation	imitación
impairment	impedimento
imperative	imperativo
imperfect tense	tiempo imperfecto
indefinite article	articulo indefinido
indirect object	objeto indirecto
individual education program	programa de educación individualizado
individualized instruction	instrucción individualizado
infection	infección
inference	inferencia
inflectional ending	inflexión final
informal inventory	inventario informal
inner ear	oído interno

inspiration	inspiración
instruction	instrucción
instructional materials	materiales de instrucción
instructional objective	objetivo instruccional
instructional program	programa de instrucción
intellect	intelecto
intellectual capacity	capacidad intelectual
intelligence	inteligencia
interaction	interacción
interpersonal relationships	relaciones interpersonales
interpretation of scores	interpretación de puntajes
interpreter	intérprete, traductor
interrogatives	interrogativos
intonation	entonación
irregular verbs	verbos irregulares

L

labial phoneme	fonema labial
labiodental	labiodental
language abilities	habilidades lingüisticas
language acquisition	adquisición del lenguaje
language components	componentes del lenguaje
language comprehension	comprensión del lenguaje
language deficit	déficit del lenguaje
language delay	retraso del lenguaje
language development	desarrollo del lenguaje
language disability	discapacidad del lenguaje
language disorder	trastorno de lenguaje
language disordered	desordenado lingüisticamente
language evaluation	evaluación del lenguaje
language game	juego lingüistico
language loss	pérdida de lenguaje
language minority student	estudiante de una minoría lingüística

language pathology	patololgía del lenguaje
language problem	problema del lenguaje
language proficiency	proficiencia de lenguaje
language quotient	cociente de lenguaje
language sample	muestra de lenguaje
language score	puntuación del lenguaje
language skills	destrezas del lenguaje
language test	prueba de lenguaje
language therapy	terapia del lenguaje
laryngeal	laríngeo
laryngeal cancer	cáncer laríngeo
laryngectomy	laringectomía
laryngitis	laringitis
laryngology	laringología
laryngoscopy	laringoscopía
laryngotomy	laringotomía
larynx	laringe
lateral lisp	ceceo lateral
learning disability	incapacidad de aprendizaje

learning handicapped student	estudiante con deficiencias en el aprendizaje
learning style	estilo de aprendizaje
least restrictive educational environment	ambiente de educación menos restrictivo
lesson	lección
lesson plan	plan de lecciones
letter reversals	inversión al escribir las letras
letters of the alphabet	letras del alfabeto
level of proficiency	nivel de proficiencia
lexeme	lexema
lexicon	léxico
linguist	lingüista
linguistic	lingüístico
linguistic approach	acercamiento lingüístico
linguistic consciousness	conciencia lingüística
linguistic contexts	contextos lingüísticos
linguistic dominance	dominancia lingüística
linguistics	lingüística
lip	labio
lipreading	lectura labial

listening comprehension	comprensión auditiva
literacy	alfabetismo

M

main idea	idea principal
mainstream English	inglés de uso común
malocclusion	oclusión defectuosa
manner of articulation	modo de articulación
mannerism	manerismo
maturation	maduración
mean length of utterance	promedio de palabras por frase
mean score	puntaje promedio
meaning	sentido
measurement	medición
medical examination	examen médico
memory	memoria

mental age	edad mental
mental deficiency	deficiencia mental
mental disorder	trastorno mental
mental health	salud mental
mental retardation	retardo mental
mentally retarded	retardado mental, retrasado mental
metalinguistic	metalingüística
middle ear	oído medio
middle ear infection	infección de oído medio
minimal brain damage	daño cerebral mínimo
modality	modalidad
monolingual	monolingüe
monologue	monólogo
monotone	monótono
morpheme	morfema
morphological analysis	análisis morfológico
morphology	morfología
morphophoneme	morfofonema
motor aphasia	afasia motora

motor coordination	coordinación motriz
multidisciplinary	multidisciplinario
muscular movement	movimiento muscular
mutism	mutismo

N

nasal	nasal
nasal cavity	cavidad nasal
nasal emission	emisión nasal
nasality	nasalidad
nasalize	nasalizar
nasopharyngeal	nasofaríngeo
national norms	normas nacionales
native language	lengua materna, lengua nativa
neologism	neologismo
nervous system	sistema nervioso

neurological	neurológico
neurological disorder	trastorno neurológico
neurological evaluation	evaluación neurológica
neurologist	neurólogo
nodule	nódulo
nonorganic speech impairment	deterioro del habla no organico
nonverbal behavior	conducta no verbal
nonverbal child	niño que no habla
nonverbal intelligence	inteligencia no verbal
nonverbal test	prueba no verbal
norm group	grupa de norma
normative scores	puntajes normativos
norm-referenced test	prueba normativa
norms	normas
noun	nombre, sustantivo
nurse	enfermera

O

objective	objetivo
occupational therapy	terapia ocupacional
oral cavity	cavidad oral
oral communication	comunicación oral
oral comprehension	comprensión oral
oral expression	expresión oral
oral language	lenguaje oral
oral peripheral examination	examen periférico oral
oral sample	muestra oral
oral-motor exercises	ejercicios oromotores
organic	orgánico
orthography	ortografía
ossicles	huesecillos
otolaryngologist	otolaringólogo
otologist	otólogo
otology	otología

otorhinolaryngology	otorrinolaringología
otosclerosis	otoesclerosis
outer ear	oído externo
outpatient clinic	clínica de consulta externa

P

palatalize	palatalizar
palatal prosthesis	prótesis palatina
palate	paladar
papilloma	papiloma
paragraph	párrafo
paragraph comprehension	comprensión de párrafos
paragraph reading	lectura de párrafos
paralysis	parálisis
paraplegia	paraplegia
participle	participio

passive voice	voz pasiva
past tense	tiempo pasado
pathologist	patólogo
pathology	patología
percent	porciento
percentage	porcentaje
percentile	percentil
percentile rank profile	perfil de rango de percentiles
percentile score	puntaje percentil
perception	percepción
perceptual-motor skills	aptitudes perceptivomotoras
perforated eardrum	tímpano perforado, tímpano roto
performance	rendimiento
personal pronoun	pronombre personal
pervasive developmental disorder	trastorno penetrante del desarrollo
pharyngeal flap operation	operación del colgajo faríngeo
pharynx	faringe
phonate	articular, enunciar
phonation	fonación

phoneme	fonema
phonemic awareness	capacidad de reconocer fonemas
phonemics	fonémica
phonetic	fonético
phonetic alphabet	alfabeto fonético
phonetic analysis	análisis fonético
phonetic transcription	transcripción fonética
phonetics	fonética
phonic	fónico
phonological	fonológico
phonological deviation	desviación fonológico
phonological process	proceso fonológico
phonology	fonología
phrase	frase
phrase production	producción de frases
physical appearance	apariencia física
physical impairment	impedimento físico
physical therapy	fisioterapia
physician	médico, doctor

picture vocabulary	vocabulario pictórico
pitch	tono
placement	colocación
plastic surgery	cirugía plástica
plosive	oclusiva
plural	plural
point of articulation	punto de articulación
polyglot	políglota
polyp	pólipo
possessive	posesivo
pragmatic	pragmático
prefix	prefijo
preposition	preposición
prepositional phrase	frase preposicional
present indicative	presente indicativo
present progressive	presente progresivo
present tense	tiempo presente
preterite tense	tiempo pretérito
primary language	lenguaje primario

problem-solving ability	habilidad de resolver problemas
procedures	procedimientos
processing	procesamiento
proficiency	proficiencia
proficiency level	nivel de proficiencia
prognosis	prognosis, pronóstico
programmed instruction	instrucción programada
progress	progreso
pronoun	pronombre
pronunciation	pronunciación
prose	prosa
prosthesis	prótesis
protocol	protocolo
proverb	proverbio
psycholinguist	psicolingüista
psycholinguistic	psicolingüística
psychological	psicológico
psychologist	psicólogo
psychology	psicólogia

psychopathology	psicopatología
psychotic	psicótico
public school	escuela pública
punctuation	puntuación

Q

quadraplegic	cuadriplégico

R

raw score	puntaje neto, puntaje bruto
readiness test	prueba de preparación
reading	lectura
reading age	edad de lectura

reading comprehension	comprensión de la lectura
reading disability	discapacidad de lectura
reading disorder	trastorno de lectura
reading quotient	cociente de lectura
reading readiness	disposición de lectura
reading skills	destrezas de lectura
reading skills acquisition	adquisición de destrezas de lectura
reading test	prueba de lectura
reading vocabulary	vocabulario de lectura
reasoning	razonamiento
receptive language	lenguaje receptivo
receptive mode	modo receptivo
receptive vocabulary	vocabulario receptivo
record form	hoja de registro
recovery	recuperación
referral date	fecha de referencia
reflexive	reflexivo
reflexive verb	verbo reflexivo
regular verb	verbo regular

rehabilitation	rehabilitación
reliability	confiabilidad
remediate	poner remedio
resonance	resonancia
resonance cavities	cavidades de resonancia
resource specialist	especialista en recursos
respiration	respiración
respirator	respirador
respiratory disease	enfermedad de las vías respiratorias
respiratory system	sistema respiratorio
retarded	retardado
rhinolalia	rinolalia
rhythm	ritmo

S

school year	año escolar
score	puntaje, puntuación
second language	segundo idioma, segunda lengua
second language acquisition	adquisición de una segunda lengua
self confidence	confianza en sí mismo
semantics	semántica
sensorimotor development	desarrollo sensorimotor
sensorineural hearing loss	pérdida de audición sensorineural
sensorineural impairment	deterioro sensorineural
sensory deprivation	privación sensorial
sensory discrimination	discriminación sensorial
sensory-motor level	nivel sensorimotor
sentence	oración
sentence completion test	prueba de terminación de oraciones
sentence comprehension	comprensión de oraciones
sentence formation	formación de oraciones

sentence interpretation	interpretación de oraciones
sentence lists	listas de oraciones
sentence production	producción de oraciones
sentence repetition test	prueba de repetición de oraciones
sequence	secuencia
sequential memory	memoria secuencial
severe mental retardation	retardo mental severo
short term memory	memoria inmediata
shyness	timidez
sibilant	sibilante
sign language	lenguaje de los signos
significance level	nivel de significación
silent reading	lectura silenciosa
skill	destreza
social competence	competencia social
social interaction	interacción social
socio-cultural	socio-cultural
socio-cultural experiences	experiencias socio-culturales
socio-cultural factors	factores socio-culturales

soft palate	paladar blando, velo palatino
sound	sonido
sound intensity	intensidad del sonido
sound wave	onda sonora
spanish proficiency	proficiencia en español
Spanish-American	hispanoamericano
spastic dysphonia	disfonía espástica
spatial discrimination	discriminación espacial
spatial orientation	orientación espacial
spatial relations	relaciones espaciales
special education	educación especial
special education program	programa de educación especial
special instruction	instrucción especial
special needs	necesidades especiales
special needs student	estudiante con necesidades especiales
special services	servicios especiales
specialist	especialista
specific language disability	discapacidad del lenguaje específica
specific learning disability	discapacidad del aprendizaje específica

speech	habla
speech act	acto del habla
speech and hearing clinic	clínica de habla y oído
speech and language disorder	trastorno de habla y lenguaje
speech and language evaluation	evaluación de habla y lenguaje
speech and language remediation program	programa correctivo de habla y lenguaje
speech audiometry	audiometría del habla
speech block	bloqueo del habla
speech defect	defecto del habla
speech development	desarrollo del habla
speech disorder	trastorno del habla
speech function	función del habla
speech impaired	impedido del habla
speech impairment	deterioro del habla
speech intelligibility	claridad al hablar
speech pathology	patología del habla
speech perception	percepción del habla
speech problem	problema del habla
speech production	producción del habla

speech reception threshold	umbral de recepción del habla
speech rehabilitation	rehabilitación del habla
speech remediation	remedio del habla, corrección del habla
speech therapy	terapia del habla
speech-language pathologist	patólogo del habla y el lenguaje
speech-reading	lectura del habla
spoken language	lenguaje hablado
spoken language disorder	trastorno del lenguaje hablado
spontaneous language	lenguaje espontaneo
standard deviation	desviación estándar
standard dialect	dialecto estándar
standard error	error estándar
standard score	puntaje estándar
standardized measure	medida estandarizada
standardized test	prueba estandarizada
statistical analysis	análisis estadístico
stoma	estoma
stop consonants	consonantes oclusivas
story details	detalles del cuento

stress (emphasis on words)	énfasis
stroke	golpe (de émbolo)
structural proficiency	proficiencia estructural
structure	estructura
stutter	tartamudear
stutterer	tartamudo
stuttering	tartamudez
subjunctive	subjuntivo
submucosal cleft	hendidura submucosa
subskill	subdestreza
subtest	subprueba
suffix	sufijo
superlative	superlativo
surface structure	estructura superficial
surgery	cirugía
survival vocabulary	vocabulario esencial para la vida cotidiana
swallow	tragar(se)
swallowing exercises	ejercicios de tragar
swallowing problems	problemas de tragar

syllable	sílabo
syllable reduction	omisión de sílabas
symbol	símbolo
symbolize	simbolizar
symptom	síntoma
syndrome	síndrome
synonym	sinónimo
syntactic	sintáctico
syntactic structure	estructura sintáctica
syntax	sintaxis

T

teacher	maestra, maestro
teaching	enseñanza
teaching methods	métodos de enseñanza
telegraphic speech	habla telegráfica

tense (of verbs)	tiempo
test	prueba, examen
test battery	batería de pruebas
test score	puntuación de prueba
test standardization	estandarización de prueba
therapeutic	terapéutico
therapist	terapeuta, terapista
therapy	terapia
thinking	pensamiento
thinking disorder	trastorno de pensamiento
threshold	umbral
throat	garganta
thrombosis	trombosis
tinnitus	tinnitus
tone	tono
tongue	lengua
tongue depressor	abatelengua
total communication approach	método de comunicación multisensorial
total score	puntaje total

trachea	tráquea
tracheoscopy	traqueoscopía
tracheotomy	traqueotomía
tracheotomy tube	tubo de traqueotomía
trainable mentally retarded	retardado mental entrenable
transcribe	transcribir
translate	traducir
translation	traducción
traumatic aphasia	afasia traumática
treatment	tratamiento
trill	vibrante múltiple
tympanic membrane	membrana del tímpano
tympanotomy	timpanotomía

U

ulcer	úlcera
utterance	enunciación

V

validity	validez
velar	velar
velopharyngeal closure	cierre velofaríngeo
velopharyngeal incompetence	incompetencia velofaríngea
velum	velo del paladar
verb	verbo
verbal ability	habilidad verbal
verbal amnesia	amnesia verbal
verbal concept	concepto verbal
verbal expression	expresión verbal
verbal processing	procesamiento verbal
verbal reasoning	razonamiento verbal
verbal scale	escala verbal
visual discrimination	discriminación visual
visual memory	memoria visual
visual perception	percepción visual

visual recognition	reconocimiento visual
visually impaired	discapacidad visual
vocabulary	vocabulario
vocabulary comprehension	comprensión de vocabulario
vocabulary development	desarrollo de vocabulario
vocabulary test	prueba de vocabulario
vocal emission	emisión vocal
vocal fatigue	fatiga vocal
vocal fold	cuerda vocal
vocal nodules	nódulos vocales
vocal tract	tracto vocal
vocalic	vocálico
vocalization	vocalización
vocalize	vocalizar
voice	voz
voice disorder	trastorno de voz
voice quality	calidad de voz
voice therapist	terapeuta de voz
voiced consonants	consonantes sonoras

voiceless consonants	consonantes sordas
vowel	vocal

W

wheelchair	silla de ruedas
whisper	cuchichear
whispered speech	habla susurrada
whole-word method	método de palabra completa
word	palabra
word association test	prueba de asociación de palabras
word endings	terminaciones de las palabras
word identification	identificación de la palabra
word lists	listas de palabras
word order	orden gramatical
word perception	percepción de palabras
word production	producción de palabras

word recognition	reconocimiento de palabras
word recognition skills	destrezas de reconocimiento de palabras
word retrieval skills	capacidad de recordar palabras
worksheet	hojas de trabajo
written communication	comunicación escrito
written expression	expresión escrita
written language	lenguaje escrito
written language test	prueba de lenguaje escrito
written sample	muestra escrita

Y

yes-no questions	preguntas de sí-no

Part 2

Spanish-English

A

abatelengua	tongue depressor
abducción	abduction
abuso de niños	child abuse
académico	academic
accidente cerebrovascular	cerebrovascular accident
acento	accent
acento extranjero	foreign accent
acercamiento cognitivo	cognitive approach
acercamiento conductual	behavioral approach
acercamiento lingüístico	linguistic approach
actividades de la vida cotidiana	activities of daily living
acto del habla	speech act
acústica	acoustics
adducción	adduction
adjetivo	adjective
adquisición de destrezas de lectura	reading skills acquisition

adquisición de una segunda lengua	second language acquisition
adquisición del lenguaje	language acquisition
adverbio	adverb
afasia	aphasia
afasia amnésica	amnesic aphasia
afasia de Broca	Broca's aphasia
afasia del desarrollo	developmental aphasia
afasia global	global aphasia
afasia motora	motor aphasia
afasia traumática	traumatic aphasia
afásico	aphasic
afonía	aphonia
afónico	aphonic
africada	affricate
aglosia	aglossia
agnosia	agnosia
agrafia	agraphia
agramatismo	agrammatism
agudeza	acuity

agudeza auditiva	auditory acuity
alalia	alalia
alfabetismo	literacy
alfabeto	alphabet
alfabeto fonético	phonetic alphabet
alófono	allophone
alomorfo	allomorph
alveolar	alveolar
ambiente	environment
ambiente de educación menos restrictivo	least restrictive educational environment
amnesia verbal	verbal amnesia
amplificación	amplification
análisis de varianza	analysis of variance
análisis estadístico	statistical analysis
análisis fonético	phonetic analysis
análisis morfológico	morphological analysis
analogía	analogy
anartria	anarthria
aneurisma	aneurism

año escolar	school year
anomia	anomia
anormal	abnormal
anormalidad	abnormality
anormalidad congénita	congenital abnormality
ansiedad	anxiety
antónimo	antonym
apariencia física	physical appearance
apraxia	apraxia
apráxico	apraxic
aprovechamiento	achievement
aptitud	aptitude
aptitudes perceptivomotoras	perceptual-motor skills
articulación	articulation
articular	articulate, phonate
artículo definido	definite article
artículo indefinido	indefinite article
asimilación	assimilation
asma	asthma

asociación auditiva	auditory association
aspirar	aspirate
ataque de ansiedad	anxiety attack
atraso del desarrollo	developmental delay
audible	audible
audición	audition, hearing
audífono	hearing aid
audiograma	audiogram
audiograma de conducción osea	bone conduction audiogram
audiología	audiology
audiólogo	audiologist
audiometría	audiometry
audiometría del habla	speech audiometry
audiómetro	audiometer
autismo	autism
autístico	autistic

B

balbuceo	babbling
batería de pruebas	test battery
bilabial	bilabial
bilingüe	bilingual
bilingüe balanceado	balanced bilingual
bilingüismo	bilingualism
bloqueo del habla	speech block

C

calidad de voz	voice quality
cambio de código	code switching
cáncer laríngeo	laryngeal cancer
capacidad de concentración	attention span

capacidad de reconocer fonemas	phonemic awareness
capacidad de recordar palabras	word retrieval skills
capacidad intelectual	intellectual capacity
capacidad para decodificar	decoding skills
categorías conceptuales	conceptual categories
cavidad nasal	nasal cavity
cavidad oral	oral cavity
cavidades de resonancia	resonance cavities
ceceo lateral	lateral lisp
centro diagnóstico	diagnostic center
cerebelo	cerebellum
Certificado de Competencia Clínica	Certificate of Clinical Competence
cierre velofaríngeo	velopharyngeal closure
circunlocución	circumlocution
cirugía	surgery
cirugía plástica	plastic surgery
claridad al hablar	speech intelligibility
clasificación	classification
clasificar	classify

cláusula	clause
clínica	clinic
clínica de consulta externa	outpatient clinic
clínica de habla y oído	speech and hearing clinic
clínico	clinician
cociente de lectura	reading quotient
cociente de lenguaje	language quotient
coclea	cochlea
codificar	encode
código	code
cognición	cognition
cognoscitivo	cognitive
colocación	placement
colocación educativa	educational placement
comparativo	comparative
compensación	compensation
competencia	competence
competencia comunicativa	communicative competence
competencia social	social competence

componentes del lenguaje	language components
comportamiento	behavior
comprensión	comprehension
comprensión auditiva	listening comprehension
comprensión de la lectura	reading comprehension
comprensión de oraciones	sentence comprehension
comprensión de párrafos	paragraph comprehension
comprensión de vocabulario	vocabulary comprehension
comprensión del lenguaje	language comprehension
comprensión oral	oral comprehension
comunicación	communication
comunicación aumentativa y alternativa	augmentative and alternative communication
comunicación oral	oral communication
comunidad bilingüe	bilingual community
concepto	concept
concepto verbal	verbal concept
conceptualización	conceptualization
conciencia lingüística	linguistic consciousness
condicional	conditional

conducción	conduction
conducción aérea	air conduction
conducción osea	bone conduction
conducta adaptativa	adaptive behavior
conducta agresiva	aggressive behavior
conducta antisocial	antisocial behavior
conducta auditiva	auditory behavior
conducta de masticación	chewing behavior
conducta emocional	emotional behavior
conducta no verbal	nonverbal behavior
conducta propia del autismo	autistic-like behavior
confiabilidad	reliability
confianza	confidence
confianza en sí mismo	self confidence
congénito	congenital
conjugación	conjugation
conjunción	conjunction
conjunto de consonantes	consonant cluster
conocimiento cultural	cultural awareness

consonante	consonant
consonantes oclusivas	stop consonants
consonantes sonoras	voiced consonants
consonantes sordas	voiceless consonants
construcción	construction
contexto	context
contextos lingüísticos	linguistic contexts
conversación	conversation
coordinación motriz	motor coordination
cópula	copula
criterio	criterion
criterios de eligibilidad	eligibility criteria
crónico	chronic
cuadriplégico	quadraplegic
cuadro clínico	clinical profile
cuadro de conducta	behavior chart
cuerda vocal	vocal cord, vocal fold
cultura	culture
culturalmente desventajado	culturally deprived

D

daño cerebral mínimo	minimal brain damage
datos	data
decibel	decibel
decodificar	decode
decoding skills	capacidad para decodificar
defecto	defect
defecto de nacimiento	birth defect
defecto del habla	speech defect
deficiencia	deficit, deficiency
deficiencia mental	mental deficiency
déficit del desarrollo	developmental deficit
déficit del lenguaje	language deficit
definición	definition
deformidad	deformity
deletreo dactilar	fingerspelling
demencia	dementia

demostrativo	demonstrative
depresión	depression
desarrollo	development
desarrollo de niños	child development
desarrollo del habla	speech development
desarrollo del lenguaje	language development
desarrollo del vocabulario	vocabulary development
desarrollo gramatical	grammatical development
desarrollo sensorimotor	sensorimotor development
desorden	disorder
desorden comunicativo	communicative disorder
desordenado lingüisticamente	language disordered
destreza	skill
destrezas auditivas	auditory skills
destrezas básicas	basic skills
destrezas de comunicación	communication skills
destrezas de lectura	reading skills
destrezas de reconocimiento de palabras	word recognition skills
destrezas del lenguaje	language skills

destrezas funcionales de lectura	functional reading skills
desventaja	disadvantage
desviación	deviation
desviación estándar	standard deviation
desviación fonológico	phonological deviation
desviar	deviate
detalles del cuento	story details
deterioro del habla	speech impairment
deterioro del habla no organico	nonorganic speech impairment
deterioro sensorineural	sensorineural impairment
diagnosis	diagnosis
diagnosticar	diagnose
dialéctico	dialectical
dialecto	dialect
dialecto estándar	standard dialect
dialectología	dialectology
diálogo	dialogue
diferencias en dialectos	dialect differences
dificultades communicativas	communicative difficulties

dígrafo	digraph
diploacusia	diplacusis
diplofonía	diplophonia
diptongo	diphthong
disacusia	disacusis
disartria	dysarthria
discapacidad de lectura	reading disability
discapacidad del aprendizaje específica	specific learning disability
discapacidad del desarrollo	developmental disability
discapacidad del lenguaje	language disability
discapacidad del lenguaje específica	specific language disability
discapacidad visual	visually impaired
discriminación	discrimination
discriminación auditiva	auditory discrimination
discriminación espacial	spatial discrimination
discriminación sensorial	sensory discrimination
discriminación visual	visual discrimination
disfagia	dysphagia
disfasia	dysphasia

disfonía	dysphonia
disfonía espástica	spastic dysphonia
disfunción	dysfunction
disgrafia	dysgraphia
dislexia	dyslexia
disposición de lectura	reading readiness
dispraxia	dyspraxia
disturbio emocional	emotional disturbance
documentación del progreso	documentation of progress
dolor de oído	earache
dominancia cerebral	cerebral dominance
dominancia lingüística	linguistic dominance

E

ecolalia	echolalia
edad cronológica	chronological age

edad de desarrollo	developmental age
edad de lectura	reading age
edad de logro	achievement age
edad mental	mental age
educable	educable
educación	education
educación bilingüe	bilingual education
educación especial	special education
educador	educator
egocéntrico	egocentric
ejercicios de tragar	swallowing exercises
ejercicios oromotores	oral-motor exercises
electroencefalógrafo	electroencephalograph
electroencefalograma	electroencephalogram
embolia	embolism
emisión nasal	nasal emission
emisión vocal	vocal emission
encadenamiento auditivo	auditory sequencing
encefalitis	encephalitis

enfasis	stress
enfermedad	disease, illness
enfermedad de Alzheimer	Alzheimer's disease
enfermedad de las vías respiratorias	respiratory disease
enfermera	nurse
enriquecimiento	enrichment
enseñanza	teaching
enseñanza diagnóstica	diagnostic teaching
entonación	intonation
entrenamiento auditivo	auditory training
enunciación	utterance, enunciation
epiglotis	epiglottis
epilepsia	epilepsy
equipo de paladar hendido	cleft palate team
equivalente de edad	age equivalent
error	error
error de articulación	articulation error
error estándar	standard error
escala de edad	age scale

escala verbal	verbal scale
escalas del desarrollo	developmental scales
escuela pública	public school
esófago	esophagus
especialista	specialist
especialista bilingüe	bilingual specialist
especialista en recursos	resource specialist
espectro autista	autism spectrum
estandarización de prueba	test standardization
estilo cognitivo	cognitive style
estilo de aprendizaje	learning style
estilo de comunicación	communication style
estimulación auditiva	auditory stimulation
estoma	stoma
estructura	structure
estructura profunda	deep structure
estructura sintáctica	syntactic structure
estructura superficial	surface structure
estructuras gramaticales	grammatical structures

estudiante con deficiencias en el aprendizaje	learning handicapped student
estudiante con necesidades especiales	special needs student
estudiante de una minoría lingüística	language minority student
etapa del desarrollo	developmental stage
etiología	etiology
etnico	ethnic
evaluación	evaluation
evaluación audiologica	audiological evaluation
evaluación bilingüe	bilingual assessment
evaluación clínica	clinical assessment
evaluación de habla y lenguaje	speech and language evaluation
evaluación de la salud	health assessment
evaluación del desarrollo	developmental assessment
evaluación del lenguaje	language evaluation
evaluación educacional	educational assessment
evaluación neurológica	neurological evaluation
examen	test, examination
examen de aptitud	ability test
examen médico	medical examination

examen periférico oral	oral peripheral examination
examinador	examiner
experiencias socio-culturales	socio-cultural experiences
expresión	expression
expresión automatica	automatic expression
expresión de ideas	idea expression
expresión escrita	written expression
expresión oral	oral expression
expresión verbal	verbal expression
expresivo	expressive

F

factores socio-culturales	socio-cultural factors
falsete	falsetto
falta de fluidez	dysfluency
faringe	pharynx
fatiga vocal	vocal fatigue

fecha de nacimiento	birthdate
fecha de referencia	referral date
fisioterapia	physical therapy
fluencia	fluency
fonación	phonation
fonema	phoneme
fonema labial	labial phoneme
fonémica	phonemics
fonética	phonetics
fonético	phonetic
fónico	phonic
fonología	phonology
fonológico	phonological
forma del lenguaje	form of language
formación de oraciones	sentence formation
frase	phrase
frase preposicional	prepositional phrase
fricativa	fricative
función del habla	speech function

G

garganta	throat
genétic	genetic
genétics	genetics
gerundio	gerund
gesto	gesture
glotal	glottal
glotis	glottis
golpe (de émbolo)	stroke
grado	grade
grado actual de desarrollo	functional level
grado de colocación	grade placement
gramática	grammar
gramatical	grammatical
gramaticalmente correcto	grammatically correct
grupa de norma	norm group
grupo consonántico	cluster
grupo étnico	ethnic group

H

habilidad	ability
habilidad cognoscitiva	cognitive ability
habilidad de resolver problemas	problem-solving ability
habilidad motora de los músculos gruesos	gross motor skills
habilidad verbal	verbal ability
habilidades lingüísticas	language abilities, linguistic abilities
habla	speech
habla automática	automatic speech
habla susurrada	whispered speech
habla telegráfica	telegraphic speech
hemiplejia	hemiplegia
hemisferio cerebral	cerebral hemisphere
hendidura	cleft
hendidura submucosa	submucosal cleft
hereditario	hereditary
hipernasalidad	hypernasality

hiponasalidad	hyponasality
hispano	Hispanic
hispanoamericano	Spanish-American
historia del desarrollo	developmental history
hito del desarrollo	developmental milestone
hoja de registro	record form
hoja de trabajo	worksheet
huesecillos	ossicles

I

idea principal	main idea
identificación de la palabra	word identification
idioglosia	idioglossia
imitación	imitation
impedido	handicapped
impedido del habla	speech impaired

impedimento	impairment, handicap
impedimento auditivo	hearing impairment
impedimento físico	physical impairment
imperativo	imperative
implante coclear	cochlear implant
incapacidad	disability
incapacidad de aprendizaje	learning disability
incapacitado	disabled
incompetencia velofaríngea	velopharyngeal incompetence
infección	infection
infección de oído medio	middle ear infection
inferencia	inference
inflexión final	inflectional ending
inglés como segundo lengua	English as a second language
inglés de uso común	mainstream English
inspiración	inspiration
instrucción	instruction
instrucción especial	special instruction
instrucción individualizado	individualized instruction

instrucción programado	programmed instruction
instrumento diagnóstico	diagnostic instrument
intelecto	intellect
inteligencia	intelligence
inteligencia no verbal	nonverbal intelligence
intensidad del sonido	sound intensity
interacción	interaction
interacción social	social interaction
interpretación de oraciones	sentence interpretation
interpretación de puntajes	interpretation of scores
intérprete	interpreter
interrogativos	interrogatives
intervención educacional	educational intervention
inventario informal	informal inventory
inversión al escribir las letras	letter reversals
juego lingüistico	language game

L

labilidad emocional	emotional lability
labio	lip
labio hendido	cleft lip
labiodental	labiodental
laringe	larynx
laringe artificial	artificial larynx
laringectomía	laryngectomy
laríngeo	laryngeal
laringitis	laryngitis
laringología	laryngology
laringoscopía	laryngoscopy
laringotomía	laryngotomy
lección	lesson
lectura	reading
lectura de párrafos	paragraph reading
lectura del desarrollo	developmental reading

lectura del habla	speech-reading
lectura labial	lipreading
lectura silenciosa	silent reading
lengua	tongue
lengua materna	home language
lengua nativa	native language
lenguaje cultural	cultural language
lenguaje de los signos	sign language
lenguaje de señas estadounidense	American Sign Langauge
lenguaje dominante	dominant language
lenguaje escrito	written language
lenguaje espontaneo	spontaneous language
lenguaje expresivo	expressive language
lenguaje hablado	spoken language
lenguaje oral	oral language
lenguaje primario	primary language
lenguaje receptivo	receptive language
lesión cerebral	brain damage
lesión de cabeza	head injury

letras del alfabeto	letters of the alphabet
lexema	lexeme
lexico	lexicon
lingüista	linguist
lingüística	linguistics
lingüístico	linguistic
lista de comprobación	checklist
listas de oraciones	sentence lists
listas de palabras	word lists

M

maduración	maturation
maestro, maestra	teacher
mandatos	commands
manerismo	mannerism
materiales de instrucción	instructional materials

medición	measurement
médico	physician, doctor
medida educacional	educational measure
medida estandarizada	standardized measure
membrana del tímpano	tympanic membrane
memoria	memory
memoria a plazo corto activa	active short term memory
memoria auditiva	auditory memory
memoria inmediata	short term memory
memoria secuencial	sequential memory
memoria visual	visual memory
mcta anual	annual goal
metalingüistica	metalinguistic
metas	goals
método de comunicación multisensorial	total communication approach
método de palabra completa	whole-word method
métodos de enseñanza	teaching methods
mezcla auditiva	auditory blending
mezclas	blends

modalidad	modality
modismo	idiom
modo de articulación	manner of articulation
modo expresivo	expressive mode
modo receptivo	receptive mode
monolingüe	monolingual
monólogo	monologue
monótono	monotone
morfema	morpheme
morfofonema	morphophoneme
morfología	morphology
movimientos muscular	muscular movements
muestra de conversación	conversation sample
muestra de lenguaje	language sample
muestra escrita	written sample
muestra oral	oral sample
multidisciplinario	multidisciplinary
mutismo	mutism

N

nasal	nasal
nasalidad	nasality
nasalizar	nasalize
nasofaríngco	nasopharyngeal
necesidades especiales	special needs
neologismo	neologism
neurológico	neurological
neurólogo	neurologist
niño autista (niño con autismo)	autistic child (child with autism)
niño excepcional	exceptional child
niño que no habla	non-verbal child
nivel de aprovechamiento académico	educational achievement level
nivel de proficiencia	level of proficiency
nivel de significación	significance level
nivel del grado	grade level
nivel sensorimotor	sensory-motor level

niveles del desarrollo	developmental levels
nódulo	nodule
nódulos vocales	vocal nodules
norma del desarrollo	developmental norm
normas	norms
normas de edad	age norms
normas del grado	grade norms
normas nacionales	national norms

O

objetive de comportamiento	behavioral objective
objetivo	objective
objetivo instruccional	instructional objective
objeto directo	direct object
objeto indirecto	indirect object
objetos comunes	common objects

oclusión defectuosa	malocclusion
oclusiva	stop consonant
oído	ear
oído externo	outer ear
oído interno	inner ear
oído medio	middle ear
omisión de consonantes	consonant deletion
omisión de grupos consonánticos	consonant reduction
omisión de sílabas	syllable reduction
onda sonora	sound wave
operación del colgajo faríngeo	pharyngeal flap operation
oración	sentence
orden gramatical	word order
orgánico	organic
orientación espacial	spatial orientation
ortografía	orthography
osículos auditivos	auditory ossicles
otoesclerosis	otosclerosis
otolaringólogo	otolaryngologist

otología	otology
otólogo	otologist
otorrinolaringología	otorhinolaryngology

P

palabra	word
paladar	palate
paladar artificial	artificial palate
paladar blando	soft palate, velum
paladar duro	hard palate
paladar hendido	cleft palate
palatalizar	palatalize
papiloma	papilloma
parálisis	paralysis
parálisis cerebral	cerebral palsy
parálisis facial	facial paralysis

paraplegia	paraplegia
párrafo	paragraph
participio	participle
patología	pathology
patología del habla	speech pathology
patología del lenguaje	language pathology
patólogo	pathologist
patólogo del habla y el lenguaje	speech-language pathologist
pensamiento	thinking
percentil	percentile
percepción	perception
percepción auditiva	auditory perception
percepción de palabras	word perception
percepción del habla	speech perception
percepción visual	visual perception
pérdida auditiva	hearing loss
pérdida de audición sensorineural	sensorineural hearing loss
pérdida de lenguaje	language loss
perfil de desarrollo	developmental profile

perfil de rango de percentiles	percentile rank profile
plan de estudios	curriculum
plan de evaluación	assessment plan
plan de lecciones	lesson plan
plural	plural
poliglota	polyglot
pólipo	polyp
poner remedio	remediate
porcentaje	percentage
porciento	percent
posesivo	possessive
pragmático	pragmatic
prefijo	prefix
preguntas de sí-no	yes-no questions
prejuicio cultural	cultural bias
preposición	preposition
presente indicativo	present indicative
presente progresivo	present progressive
privación	deprivation

privación cultural	cultural deprivation
privación sensorial	sensory deprivation
problema del habla	speech problem
problema del lenguaje	language problem
problemas de tragar	swallowing problems
procedimiento diagnóstico	diagnostic procedure
procedimientos	procedures
procedimientos clínicos	clinical procedures
procesamiento	processing
procesamiento auditivo	auditory processing
procesamiento verbal	verbal processing
proceso fonológico	phonological process
producción de frases	phrase production
producción de oraciones	sentence production
producción de palabras	word production
producción del habla	speech production
proficiencia	proficiency
proficiencia de lenguaje	language proficiency
proficiencia en español	spanish proficiency

proficiencia estructural	structural proficiency
prognosis	prognosis
programa bilingüe	bilingual program
programa correctivo de habla y lenguaje	speech and language program
programa de educación especial	special education program
programa de educación individualizado	individual education program
programa de instrucción	instructional program
programa educacional	educational program
progreso	progress
promedio de palabras por frase	mean length of utterance
pronombre	pronoun
pronombre personal	personal pronoun
pronunciación	pronunciation
prosa	prose
prótesis	prosthesis
prótesis palatina	palatal prosthesis
protocolo	protocol
proverbio	proverb
prueba	test

prueba con referencia a criterios	criterion-referenced test
prueba de articulación	articulation test
prueba de asociación de palabras	word association test
prueba de audición	hearing test
prueba de lectura	reading test
prueba de lenguaje	language test
prueba de lenguaje escrito	test of written language
prueba de nivel	achievement test
prueba de preparación	readiness test
prueba de repetición de oraciones	sentence repetition test
prueba de terminación de oraciones	sentence completion test
prueba de vocabulario	vocabulary test
prueba diagnóstica	diagnostic test
prueba estandarizada	standardized test
prueba no verbal	nonverbal test
prueba normativa	norm-referenced test
pruebas alternativas de evaluación	alternative assessments
psicolingüista	psycholinguist
psicolingüística	psycholinguistic

psicólogia	psychology
psicológico	psychological
psicólogo	psychologist
psicopatología	psychopathology
psicótico	psychotic
puntaje	score
puntaje de edad	age score
puntaje del grado equivalente	grade equivalent score
puntaje estándar	standard score
puntaje neto	raw score
puntaje normativo	normative score
puntaje percentil	percentile score
puntaje promedio	mean score
puntaje total	total score
punto de articulación	point of articulation
puntuación de prueba	test score
puntuación del lenguaje	language score

R

razonamiento	reasoning
razonamiento verbal	verbal reasoning
recepción auditiva	auditory reception
reconocimiento de palabras	word recognition
reconocimiento visual	visual recognition
recuperación	recovery
reducción de la secuencia de consonantes	consonant sequence reduction
reflejo acústico	acoustic reflex
reflexivo	reflexive
rehabilitación	rehabilitation
rehabilitación del habla	speech rehabilitation
relaciones espaciales	spatial relations
relaciones interpersonales	interpersonal relationships
remedio del habla	speech remediation
rendimiento	performance
resonancia	resonance

respiración	respiration
respirador	respirator
respirar	breathe, respirate
retardado mental	mentally retarded
retardado mental educable	educable mentally retarded
retardado mental entrenable	trainable mentally retarded
retardo mental severo	severe mental retardation
retraso del lenguaje	language delay
retroalimentación auditiva	auditory feedback
revisión anual	annual review
rinolalia	rhinolalia
ritmo	rhythm
ronquera	hoarseness

S

salidas falsas	false starts
salud mental	mental health
secuencia	sequence
secuencia auditiva	auditory sequence
secuencia del desarrollo	developmental sequence
segunda lengua	second language
semántica	semantics
sentido	meaning
servicios educacionales	educational services
servicios especiales	special services
sibilante	sibilant
sílabo	syllable
silla de ruedas	wheelchair
simbolizar	symbolize
símbolo	symbol
síndrome	syndrome

síndrome de Down	Down Syndrome
síndrome de inmunodeficiencia adquirida	Acquired Immune Deficiency Syndrome
sinónimo	synonym
sintáctico	syntactic
sintaxis	syntax
síntoma	symptom
sistema de comunicación aumentativa	augmentative communication system
sistema nervioso	nervous system
sistema respiratorio	respiratory system
socio-cultural	socio-cultural
sonido	sound
sordera	deafness
sordo	deaf
subdestreza	subskill
subjuntivo	subjunctive
subprueba	subtest
sufijo	suffix
superlativo	superlative
sustantivo	noun

T

tartamudear	stutter
tartamudez	stuttering
tartamudo	stutterer
tcrapcuta	therapist
terapeuta de voz	voice therapist
terapéutico	therapeutic
terapia	therapy
terapia de conducta	behavior therapy
terapia de grupo	group therapy
terapia del habla	speech therapy
terapia del lenguaje	language therapy
terapia ocupacional	occupational therapy
terminaciones de las palabras	word endings
tiempo (de verbos)	tense
tiempo imperfecto	imperfect tense
tiempo pasado	past tense

tiempo presente	present tense
tiempo pretérito	preterite tense
timidez	shyness
tímpano	eardrum
tímpano perforado	perforated eardrum
timpanotomía	tympanotomy
tinnitus	tinnitus
tono	pitch, tone
tracto vocal	vocal tract
traducción	translation
traducir	translate
traductor	translator
tragar(se)	swallow
transcribir	transcribe
transcripción fonética	phonetic transcription
tráquea	trachea
traqueoscopía	tracheoscopy
traqueotomía	tracheotomy
trastorno aritmético	arithmetic disorder

trastorno cerebral	brain disorder
trastorno de ansiedad	anxiety disorder
trastorno de articulación	articulation disorder
trastorno del desarrollo de articulación	developmental articulation disorder
trastorno de atención deficiente	Attention Deficit Disorder
trastorno de conducta	behavior disorder
trastorno dc lcctura	reading disorder
trastorno del desarrollo de lectura	developmental reading disorder
trastorno de pensamiento	thinking disorder
trastorno de voz	voice disorder
trastorno del desarrollo	developmental disorder
trastorno del desarrollo de lenguaje	developmental language disorder
trastorno del desarrollo de lenguaje expresivo	developmental expressive language disorder
trastorno del desarrollo de lenguaje receptivo	developmental receptive language disorder
trastorno del desarrollo fonológico	developmental phonologic disorder
trastorno del habla	speech disorder
trastorno del habla y lenguaje	speech and language disorder
trastorno del lenguaje	language disorder
trastorno del lenguaje hablado	spoken language disorder

trastorno funcional	functional disorder
trastorno mental	mental disorder
trastorno neurológico	neurological disorder
trastorno penetrante del desarrollo	pervasive developmental disorder
trastorno perceptivo auditivo	auditory perceptual disorder
tratamiento	treatment
trauma de cabeza	head trauma
trauma de niñez	childhood trauma
traumatismo de craneal agudo	acute head trauma
trombosis	thrombosis
trompa de eustaquio	eustachian tube
tubo de traqueotomía	tracheotomy tube
tumor cerebral	brain tumor

U

ulcera	ulcer
umbral	threshold

umbral de conducción aérea	air conduction threshold
umbral de conducción osea	bone conduction threshold
umbral de recepción del habla	speech reception threshold
uso funcional del lenguaje	functional use of language

V

validez	validity
validez del contenido	content validity
validez relacionada con criterios	criterion-related validity
velar	velar
velo del paladar	velum
verbo	verb
verbo irregular	irregular verb
verbo reflexivo	reflexive verb
verbo regular	regular verb
vía respíratoria	airway

vibrante múltiple	trill
vocabulario	vocabulary
vocabulario de lectura	reading vocabulary
vocabulario esencial para la vida cotidiana	survival vocabulary
vocabulario expresivo	expressive vocabulary
vocabulario pictórico	picture vocabulary
vocabulario receptivo	receptive vocabulary
vocal	vowel
vocálico	vocalic
vocalización	vocalization
vocalizar	vocalize
voz	voice
voz pasiva	passive voice

Appendix A
Terminology for Common Syndromes and Disabilities

Terms are listed below in English and Spanish for disabilities that often affect communication or learning.

English	Spanish
Acquired Immune Deficiency Syndrome	síndrome de inmunodeficiencia adquirida
Alzheimer's Disease	enfermedad de Alzheimer
aphasia	afasia
apraxia	apraxia
articulation disorder	trastorno de articulación
Attention Deficit Disorder	trastorno de atención deficiente
autism	autismo
cerebral palsy	parálisis cerebral
cleft palate	paladar hendido
deafness	sordera
developmental disability	discapacidad del desarrollo
Down Syndrome	síndrome de Down
dysarthria	disartria
dysphagia	disfagia
dysphasia	disfasia
epilepsy	epilepsia
hearing impairment	impedimento auditivo
language disorder	trastorno del lenguaje
mental disorder	trastorno mental
mental retardation	retardo mental

Appendix A may be reproduced for nonprofit educational use.

Source: Mattes, L. J. (2009). *Bilingual Language, Speech, and Special Education Dictionary.* Published by Academic Communication Associates, Inc., P.O. Box 4279, Oceanside, CA 92052-4279   Web: www.acawebsite.com

neurological disorder	trastorno neurológico
pervasive developmental disorder	trastorno penetrante del desarrollo
reading disability	discapacidad de lectura
sensorineural hearing loss	pérdida de audición sensorineural
specific learning disability	discapacidad del aprendizaje específica
stuttering	tartamudez
visual impairment	discapacidad visual
voice disorder	trastorno de voz

Appendix B
Terminology for Language Structures

Terms are listed below in English and Spanish for a variety of basic language structures.

English	Spanish
adjective	adjetivo
adverb	adverbio
article	artículo
comparative	comparativo
conjunction	conjunción
consonant	consonante
copula	cópula
definite article	artículo definido
imperative	imperativo
imperfect tense	tiempo imperfecto
indefinite article	artículo indefinido
indirect object	objeto indirecto
irregular verb	verbo irregular
noun	nombre, sustantivo
participle	participio

Appendix B may be reproduced for nonprofit educational use.

Source: Mattes, L. J. (2009). *Bilingual Language, Speech, and Special Education Dictionary*. Published by Academic Communication Associates, Inc., P.O. Box 4279, Oceanside, CA 92052-4279   Web: www.acawebsite.com

passive voice	voz pasiva
past tense	tiempo pasado
personal pronoun	pronombre personal
plural	plural
possessive	posesivo
prefix	prefijo
preposition	preposición
prepositional phrase	frase preposicional
present indicative	presente indicativo
present progressive	presente progresivo
present tense	tiempo presente
preterite tense	tiempo pretérito
pronoun	pronombre
reflexive verb	verbo reflexivo
regular verb	verbo regular
suffix	sufijo
superlative	superlativo
verb	verbo
vowel	vocal

References

Mattes, L. J. *Bilingual language, speech, and hearing dictionary*. (2000). (2nd Edition). Oceanside, CA: Academic Communication Associates.

Mattes, L. J. & Garcia-Easterly, I. (2007). The *bilingual speech and language intervention resource: Lists, forms, and instructional aids for Hispanic students*. Oceanside, CA: Academic Communication Associates.

Roseberry-McKibbin, C. (2008). *Multicultural students with special learning needs: Practical strategies for assessment and intervention*. (3rd edition). Oceanside, CA: Academic Communication Associates.